摇滚数学日

【美】苏·凯斯尔◎著
【美】杰瑞·史麦斯◎绘
范晓星◎译

天津出版传媒集团

新蕾出版社

献给劳拉。

——苏·凯斯尔

献给劳伦·克林纳尔。

——杰瑞·史麦斯

图书在版编目 (CIP) 数据

摇滚数学日/(美)凯斯尔(Kassirer,S.)著;(美)史麦斯(Smath,J.)绘;范晓星译.
—天津:新蕾出版社,2014.1(2024.12 重印)
(数学帮帮忙·互动版)
书名原文:Math Fair Blues
ISBN 978-7-5307-5900-4

Ⅰ.①摇…
Ⅱ.①凯…②史…③范…
Ⅲ.①数学–儿童读物
Ⅳ.①O1–49
中国版本图书馆 CIP 数据核字(2013)第 270445 号

Math Fair Blues by Sue Kassirer;
Illustrated by Jerry Smath.
Copyright © 2001 by Kane Press, Inc.
All rights reserved, including the right of reproduction in whole or in part in any form. This edition published by arrangement with Kane Press, Inc. New York, NY, represented by Lerner Publishing Group through The ChoiceMaker Korea Co. Agency.
Simplified Chinese translation copyright © 2014 by New Buds Publishing House (Tianjin) Limited Company
ALL RIGHTS RESERVED
本书中文简体版专有出版权经由中华版权代理中心授予新蕾出版社(天津)有限公司。未经许可,不得以任何方式复制或抄袭本书的任何部分。
津图登字:02-2012-227

出版发行:天津出版传媒集团
　　　　　新蕾出版社
http://www.newbuds.com.cn
地　　　址:天津市和平区西康路 35 号(300051)
出 版 人:马玉秀
电　　　话:总编办(022)23332422
　　　　　发行部(022)23332679　23332351
传　　　真:(022)23332422
经　　　销:全国新华书店
印　　　刷:天津新华印务有限公司
开　　　本:787mm×1092mm　1/16
印　　　张:3
版　　　次:2014 年 1 月第 1 版　2024 年 12 月第 25 次印刷
定　　　价:12.00 元

无处不在的数学

资深编辑　卢　江

　　人们常说"兴趣是最好的老师",有了兴趣,学习就会变得轻松愉快。数学对于孩子来说或许有些难,因为比起语文,数学显得枯燥、抽象,不容易理解,孩子往往不那么喜欢。可许多家长都知道,学数学对于孩子的成长和今后的生活有多么重要。不仅数学知识很有用,学习数学过程中获得的数学思想和方法更会影响孩子的一生,因为数学素养是构成人基本素质的一个重要因素。但是,怎样才能让孩子对数学产生兴趣呢? 怎样才能激发他们兴致勃勃地去探索数学问题呢? 我认为,让孩子读些有趣的书或许是不错的选择。读了这套"数学帮帮忙",我立刻产生了想把它们推荐给教师和家长朋友们的愿望,因为这真是一套会让孩子爱上数学的好书!

　　这套有趣的图书从美国引进,原出版者是美国资深教育专家。每本书讲述一个孩子们生活中的故事,由故事中出现的问题自然地引入一个数学知识,然后通过运用数学知识解决问题。比如,从帮助外婆整理散落的纽扣引出分类,从为小狗记录藏骨头的地点引出空间方位等等。故事素材全部来源于孩子们的真实生活，不是童话，不是幻想，而是鲜活的生活实例。正是这些发生在孩子身边的故事，让孩子们懂得，数学无处不在并且非常有用；这些鲜活的实例也使得抽象的概念更易于理解，更容易激发孩子学习数学的兴趣，让他们逐渐爱上数学。这样的教育思想和方法与我国近年来提倡的数学教育理念是十分吻合的！

这是一套适合5~8岁孩子阅读的书，书中的有趣情节和生动的插画可以将抽象的数学问题直观化、形象化，为孩子的思维活动提供具体形象的支持。如果亲子共读的话，家长可以带领孩子推测情节的发展，探讨解决难题的办法，让孩子在愉悦的氛围中学到知识和方法。

值得教师和家长朋友们注意的是，在每本书的后面，出版者还加入了"互动课堂"及"互动练习"，一方面通过一些精心设计的活动让孩子巩固新学到的数学知识，进一步体会知识的含义和实际应用；另一方面帮助家长指导孩子阅读，体会故事中数学之外的道理，逐步提升孩子的阅读理解能力。

我相信孩子读过这套书后一定会明白，原来，数学不是烦恼，不是包袱，数学真能帮大忙！

　　说到烦恼嘛，我的烦恼就是数学日，还有三天就到了。你们猜，谁还没有准备好数学项目汇报？就是我！还有我的几个朋友也没准备好。我们光忙着摇滚乐队的排练了……不过，这倒给了我一个启发！

3

"数学日那天,我们乐队能不能演奏一曲,来代替数学项目汇报呢?"第二天,我问沃尔先生,"您还记得您在讲到节奏有点儿像数学时是怎么说的吧?"

"我当然记得,赛斯。"沃尔先生说。他仔细想了想,说道:"好吧,你们可以演奏,但还是要准备数学项目汇报。"

我们第一场真正的音乐会！我的朋友们也都兴奋极了，可一想到数学项目汇报，我们就蔫儿了。唯一没有唉声叹气的就是黛娜。为什么呢？因为她的数学总是得 A。

放学后，我们到黛娜家排练。

"咱们穿什么衣服？"排练完，她问大家，"还有，咱们的乐队叫什么名字？"

黛娜是对的。我们需要一个名字、一身行头……和数学项目汇报！

"咱们穿印满酷酷图案的 T 恤衫怎么样？"乔说。

"那要花好多钱呢！"哈利边说边练习着鞠躬。

　　"有了！"黛娜说，"我们可以用我生日时得到的这套礼物印制我们自己的T恤衫。明天大家都带几件白色的T恤衫来吧。"

　　"还要想想印什么图案。"我说。

　　"还有数学项目呢！"黛娜补充道。

　　"对呀！对呀！"大家齐声说。

第二天，我们先在旧 T 恤衫上练习。幸亏我们这么做了！哈利画的吉他就像是花瓶里插了一朵花。乔弄到自己身上的颜料比印在 T 恤衫上的还要多。

　　"真让人泄气。"黛娜说,"咱们休息一会儿吧。"

　　"吃些点心怎么样?"乔说,"花生酱加果冻总能让我更好地思考。"

这招还真灵！乔突然喊道："我有主意了！"她把空果冻瓶子洗干净，用它蘸上红色颜料，然后按在她的 T 恤衫上。阿布拉卡达布拉！一个完美的红圆圈出现了！

　　"嘿!"黛娜喊起来,"我们还可以用别的瓶子呀! 大一些的,小一些的……"

　　"为什么只用瓶子呢?"哈利说,"看看这些东西,我们可以印出各种形状,三角形、正方形、长方形,什么都可以用。"

　　"喂，也不是什么都可以用。"黛娜说着，朝
我跑来。

　　"哎哟！"我拿的是她妈妈最好的水晶花瓶。

“看这个！”黛娜说。她用一块黄色的积木，印了一个轮廓清晰又漂亮的形状。那正是我想要的形状：长方形。可我了解黛娜，她一定会拿着这块积木不放手的。

"啊哈!"我看到一个小小的塑料玩具屋。它底部的大小和形状正好跟积木一样,而且,还有个很棒的提手呢!

哈利嘴里念念有词："三角形看着很好，可我找不到三角形的东西啊。"我们都帮他一起找。真是不好找。我们找到的东西不是太大了……

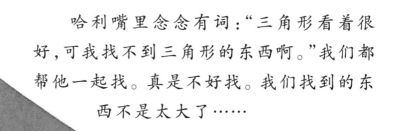

就是太容易碎了……

或者太不平整了。

还是黛娜挽回了局面。"看！"她大声喊，"这个糖果盒正合适！"

太完美了！哈利用盒盖印出绿色的三角形，用盒底印出黄色的三角形。然后我们又可以吃点心啦。

　　"嘿，你们看！"乔突然喊道。她在一个正方形上画了一条对角线。"两个三角形！"她说，"我真是个天才，对不对？"

　　我们身边居然隐藏着那么多形状啊！

最后，我们大功告成了。大家都觉得，再高级的机器印出来的 T 恤衫也不过如此吧！它们看起来漂亮极了。"每件都不一样。"黛娜说，"但放在一起又很和谐。"

第二天，我们早早儿起床，穿上我们的演出服排练。我们的演奏听起来确实不错。黛娜的小狗是个很棒的听众！

　　就在我们走着去学校时，我突然想起来一件事。
"糟糕！"我说，"我们把数学项目汇报给忘啦！"
　　"哎呀，是啊！"哈利和乔说道。
　　"已经来不及了。"黛娜说，"我只希望沃尔先生还
能同意我们演出。"

可是那天上午，沃尔先生想的是别的事。一个意想不到的数学小测验！真走运，我心想，数学是我最差的一门，我还没准备数学项目汇报呢，这又来了一个小测验！

数学难题?
来找我

沃尔先生!

可你们猜猜考的是什么？平面图形！就像我们的T恤衫上印着的那些！我们四个人互相挤挤眼睛。再猜猜接下来怎样？答案我全都知道！

我们知道，后面该是数学项目汇报的时间了。

"咱们溜吧！"哈利悄悄地说，"沃尔先生要是看不到我们，也许会把我们忘了。"

我们四个人飞快地直奔礼堂而去。

猜猜
有多少？

A B
D E

我们在后台藏好，等待着重要时刻的到来。

终于，大幕拉开了。

"欢迎各位！"校长菲利普女士说，"在颁奖之前，我们有一个特别的惊喜，就是由我们学生自己组成的摇滚乐队，他们是……"她看看我们。

数学日
颁奖典礼

　　“我们忘了给乐队起名字！”乔小声说。

　　“还忘了数学项目汇报。”黛娜说。

　　得有人救场才行！快！于是，我抓过麦克风，大声说：“我们是平面摇滚乐队！”观众们疯狂地鼓掌，我们开始演奏了。

　　他们爱死我们了！掌声此起彼伏，菲利普女士不得不请大家安静下来，好继续颁奖。

我们一坐下来，我那摇滚歌星的感觉立刻消失了。我又变成了一个普普通通的孩子——一个没有数学项目汇报的孩子。

　　我的心里七上八下，什么都没听见，直到菲利普女士大声地说道："最后一个奖是新设立的，要颁发给'最具艺术创意的数学项目'，得奖者是……

平面摇滚乐队！因为他们的 T 恤衫数学项目棒极了！"

数学项目？得奖了？我们乐队？我们简直不敢相信！我们在数学日上得奖了！

观众们大声欢呼："再来一个！再来一个！"于是我们又演奏了一曲。有一件事是肯定的——平面摇滚乐队那是相当有型啊！

31

平面图形

下面是一些平面图形。请你找出全等的图形。

全等指的是形状和大小都相同。

一个长方形有
　4 条边
　4 个角

这两个全等！

一个正方形有
　4 条边
　4 个角

这两个全等！

一个三角形有
　3 条边
　3 个角

这两个全等！

一个圆形有
　0 条边
　0 个角

这两个全等！

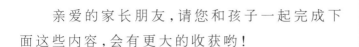

亲爱的家长朋友,请您和孩子一起完成下面这些内容,会有更大的收获哟!

提高阅读能力

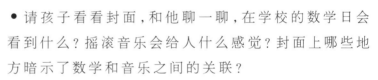

● 请孩子看看封面,和他聊一聊,在学校的数学日会看到什么?摇滚音乐会给人什么感觉?封面上哪些地方暗示了数学和音乐之间的关联?

● 读完故事后,再看一遍插图。平面摇滚乐队的几个孩子用了哪些物品来制作 T 恤衫上的彩色图案?

● 赛斯和他的朋友们每个人都为最后的项目汇报出了一份力。谁出了什么主意?黛娜家的小狗有贡献吗?(提示:答案在第 20 页上)

- 请复习第 23 页上的 4 种平面图形。请孩子数数每种图形各有几个角。黑板上的哪个图形没有角?

- 请孩子在书中找到 15 个平面图形,T 恤衫上的不算哟!

- 请看第 18 页,如果乔在正方形中间,用╳隔开,那她就有 8 个三角形了,让孩子数出这 8 个三角形。

- 让孩子比较一下第 32 页每种图形中,全等的一组和其他图形有什么不同,是大一些,小一些,还是一样大?

生活中的数学

- 制作一张包装纸。先帮孩子在硬纸板上画出一个图形,把它剪下来当作模板。再找来一大张白纸,让孩子在纸上用模板重复地描出那个图形,最后用蜡笔涂上颜色,这样一张漂亮的包装纸就做成了。

- 自制土豆印章。将两个土豆分别一切为二。把每一半土豆刻出不同的形状:正方形、圆形、长方形和三角形。把颜料倒进盘子里,用土豆印章蘸上颜料在纸上画画。

小朋友,请你给上面的图形按类别涂上颜色吧。长方形涂**红**色,正方形涂**蓝**色,三角形涂**黄**色,圆形涂**紫**色,平行四边形涂**灰**色。

把一张长方形的纸剪成大小相等的两块,你能想出几种剪法?请你在下面画出来。

第一种

第二种

第三种

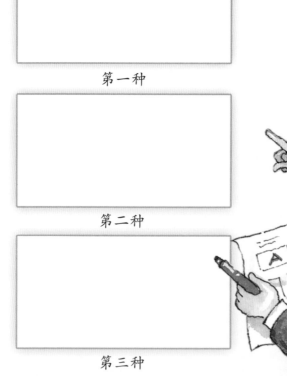

用上面的物体,能画出圆的请用圆形圈出来,能画出三角形的用三角形圈出来,能画出正方形的,用正方形圈出来,能画出长方形的,用长方形圈出来。

涂一涂

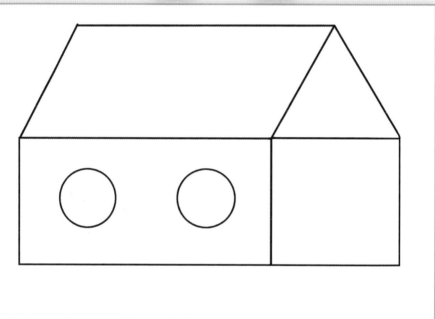

猜猜我是谁？

三角形　　圆形　　长方形　　正方形

小朋友，你能猜出躲在乔身后的是什么
图形吗？请你试着连线吧！注意，有的图形有
多种可能哟！

比比谁更大？

小朋友,你能说出哪个形状大,哪个形状小吗?

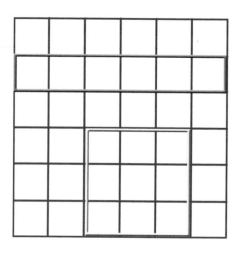

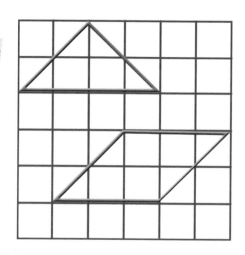

画出自己喜欢的图形

用不同平面图形拼组的汽车真漂亮。

你能用不同的平面图形画一幅自己喜欢的画吗?

41

互动练习1：

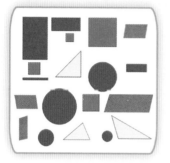

互动练习2：

方案1

方案2

方案3

互动练习3：

互动练习4：

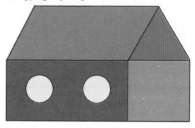

互动练习5：

三角形　圆形　长方形　正方形

互动练习6：

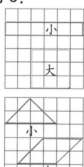

互动练习7：略

（习题设计：王　康）

Math Fair Blues

Talk about problems. Mine was called Math Fair, and it was just three days away. Guess who didn't have a project? Me. Neither did my friends. We were too busy with our new rock band...which gave me an idea!

"Could our band do a concert at the fair instead of a project?"I asked Mr.Wall the next day. "You know how you said that rhythm is kind of like math?"

"I sure did, Seth,"Mr. Wall said. He thought hard, "Okay. You can play—but you still have to do math projects."

Our first real concert! My friends were excited too—but not about the math projects. The only one who didn't moan was Dana. Why would she? She gets all A's in math.

After school we rehearsed at Dana's.

"What will we wear? "she asked when we were done."And what about name? "

Dana was right. We needed a name and a look...We also needed a math project!

"Why don't we have T-shirts printed up with cool pictures?"said Jo.

"That would cost a fortune,"Harry said, practicing his bow.

"I know!"said Dana."We can print our own shirts with this kit I got for my birthday. Everyone just bring some white T-shirts over tomorrow."

"And ideas for designs,"I said.

"And for math projects!"added Dana.

"Yeah, yeah,"we all said.

The next day we started practicing on old shirts. It was good we did! Harry's guitar came out looking like a vase with a flower in it! Jo got more paint on the shirt she was wearing than on the one she was painting.

"I'm discouraged,"Dana said."Let's take a break."

"How about a snack?"said Jo."Peanut butter and jelly always helps me think better."

It did help! Suddenly Jo cried out,"I've got it!"She washed the empty jelly jar and dipped it into the red paint. Then she pressed it onto her shirt. Abracadabra! A perfect red circle!

"Hey!"Dana shouted."We could use other jars too—bigger ones, littler ones..."

"Why only use jars?"Harry said."Look at all this stuff. We can print lots of shapes—triangles, squares, rectangles—whatever we can find."

"Well, not quite whatever,"said Dana, running over to me.

"Whoops!"I had picked up her mom's best crystal vase.

"Look at this,"said Dana. She was making a nice sharp print with a yellow block. It was just the shape I wanted—a rectangle. But I knew Dana. She'd be using it forever.

Ah-ha! I spotted a little plastic dollhouse. The bottom was the same size and shape as the block. Plus, it had a great handle!

Harry kept muttering, "Triangles would look cool. But I can't find a triangle shape."We all helped him look. It wasn't easy. The stuff we found was too big... too breakable... or too bumpy.

Dana saved the day."Look!"she yelled."This candy box is perfect!"

It was perfect. Harry used the top for green triangles and the bottom for yellow. And we all got to have another snack.

"Hey, look!"cried Jo suddenly. She drew a line across a square, from one corner to the other."Two triangles!"she said."Am I a genius, or what?"

Shapes were hiding out all over the place!

Finally we were done. And ask anyone. No fancy printer could have done a better job. The shirts looked great. "They're all different,"Dana said. "But they all go together."

We got up early the next day for our dress rehearsal. We sounded really good. And Dana's dog made a great audience!

We were walking to school when it hit me. "Oh, no!"I said. "We forgot about the math projects!"

"Uh, oh,"said Harry and Jo.

"Too late now,"said Dana."I just hope Mr. Wall still lets us perform!"

But that morning Mr. Wall had his mind on something else. A surprise quiz—in math! Just my luck, I thought. My worst subject. I have no project. And now a test!

But guess what the test was on? 2-D shapes—just like the ones on our shirts! The four of us winked at one another. Guess what again? I knew all the answers!

Next thing we knew, it was time to set up the math projects.

"Let's get out of here,"Harry whispered."Mr. Wall might forget about us if he doesn't see us."

Quickly, we made a beeline for the auditorium.

We hid backstage until our big moment.

Finally the curtain opened.

"Welcome!"said the principal, Mrs. Phillips. "Before I present the awards, we have a special surprise—our own student rock band, the...uh..."She looked at us.

"We forgot to name the band!"Jo whispered.

"On top of forgetting the math projects," said Dana.

Someone had to do something—quick. I grabbed the mike and called out,"The 2-D Rockers!" The audience clapped like mad, and we began to play.

They loved us! The clapping went on and on and on. Mrs. Phillips had to shush everybody so she could give out the awards.

As soon as we sat down, I stopped feeling like a rock star. I was a regular kid again—a kid with no math project.

I got really nervous. I didn't hear a thing until Mrs. Phillips said,"And now for our last award. It's brand new, and it's for the Most Artistic Math Project. It goes to..."

"The 2-D Rockers, for their T-shirt math project!"

Math project? Award? Us? We couldn't believe it! We had won an award in the Math Fair!

The audience yelled, "Encore! Encore!"So we played again. And one thing was for sure—the 2-D Rockers were in great shape!